THIS ANNUAL BELONGS TO

This edition published by Parragon Books Ltd in 2016

Parragon Books Ltd
Chartist House
15–17 Trim Street
Bath BA1 1HA, UK
www.parragon.com

Written and designed by Rich T Media Ltd for Parragon Books Ltd

ISBN 978-1-4748-4474-1

Printed in Poland

BATMAN

ANNUAL 2017

Batman created by Bob Kane with Bill Finger.

PaRragon

Bath · New York · Cologne · Melbourne · Delhi
Hong Kong · Shenzhen · Singapore

INSIDE

Origins Of BATMAN

The super hero saviour of Gotham City

THE BEGINNING

Bruce Wayne was only a boy when he saw his parents killed by a mugger. Young Bruce promised to fight crime on the streets of Gotham City and make the city safer. As he grew up he studied hard, built up his strength and learned a variety of martial arts. He chose to dress as a bat to strike fear into the hearts of cunning villains such as the Joker, the Penguin and Killer Croc.

AWESOME ARSENAL

Bruce's company, Wayne Enterprises, develops and builds his weapons and gadgets.

FAST FRIENDS

Batman has several allies, including Robin, his loyal sidekick, Alfred Pennyworth, his valet and Commissioner Gordon, the Gotham City police chief.

KNIGHT CALL

Batman is also known as the Caped Crusader and the Dark Knight.

ESSENTIAL DATA

REAL NAME: Bruce Wayne

APPEARANCE: Muscular, caped crime fighter

SKILLS: Extremely intelligent, Batman is a master detective. Incredibly strong, he is an expert in martial arts. He also has access to high-tech weaponry and super-speedy vehicles

WEAPON OF CHOICE: His Utility Belt includes Batarangs, smoke bombs and explosives!

Piece Of The Action!

Which four jigsaw pieces at the bottom of the page complete the picture of Batman in Gotham City?

ANSWERS ON PAGE 69

The JOKER

He's no laughing matter...

VILE VAT

Although the Joker's origins are uncertain, his green hair, white skin and manic grin are thought to be the result of falling into a vat of chemicals.

NO GOOD HOOD

Before he became the Joker, this villain was a small-time criminal known as the Red Hood.

TWO'S COMPANY

The Joker found romance with Harley Quinn, a doctor at Arkham Asylum. Quinn became his sidekick and loyal partner in crime.

ESSENTIAL DATA

REAL NAME: *Unknown*

APPEARANCE: *A colourful, crazed clown*

SKILLS: *Skilled at hand-to-hand combat, he also uses a variety of funny-looking, but deadly gadgets. These include acid flowers, exploding cigars and electrifying hand-buzzers*

WEAPON OF CHOICE: *Joker Venom, a toxic gas that leaves its victim with a hideous grin*

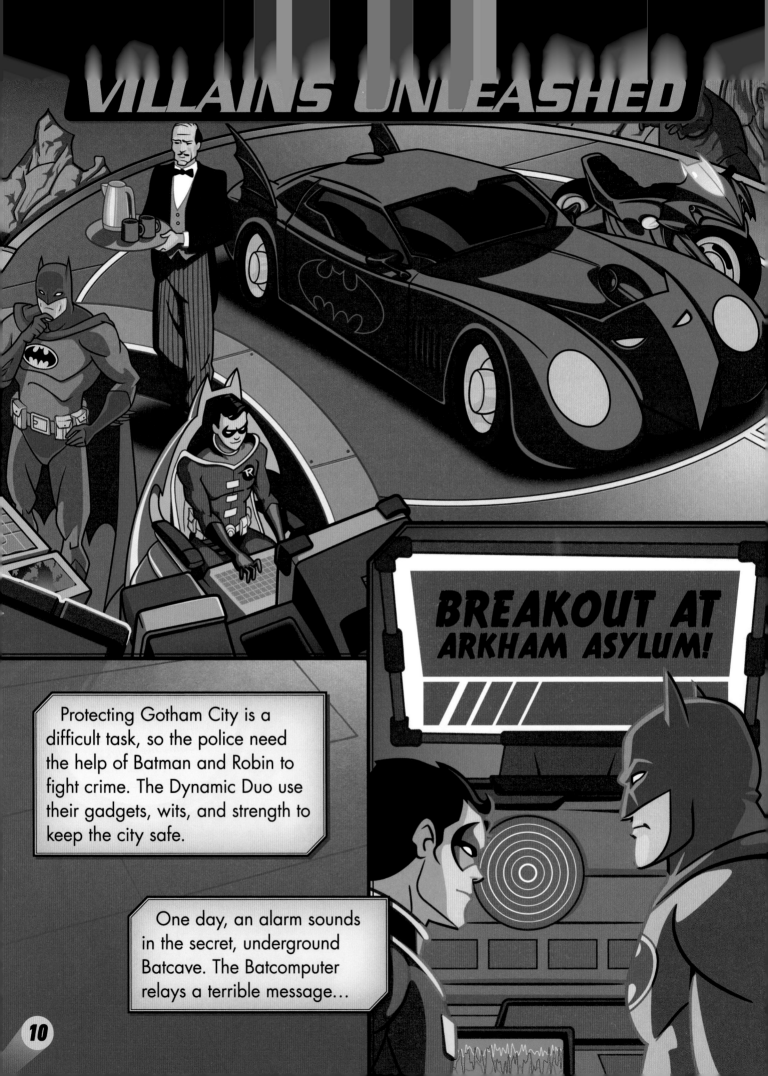

BREAKOUT AT ARKHAM ASYLUM!

Protecting Gotham City is a difficult task, so the police need the help of Batman and Robin to fight crime. The Dynamic Duo use their gadgets, wits, and strength to keep the city safe.

One day, an alarm sounds in the secret, underground Batcave. The Batcomputer relays a terrible message…

Arkham Asylum houses Gotham City's most dangerous villains… until the Joker plays the ultimate prank and busts them loose. The villains can't wait to cause chaos all over the city!

"Now that's a *punch*-line!" the crook cackles.

It's time to round up the rogues!
"To the Batmobile!" the Dark
Knight shouts.
"To the Batcycle," Robin calls out.
The Dynamic Duo zoom into action.

Robin speeds away to Gotham
State University, where the Scarecrow is
threatening to unleash his Fear Toxin.
Robin bursts into a classroom.
"Class dismissed!" Robin declares.
The Scarecrow pulls out a poison blaster.

Fitted with a gas mask, the Boy
Wonder is unaffected by the Scarecrow's
fumes. He gives the dangerous doctor
a taste of his own medicine.

Across town, Batman arrives at Gotham City Park to find that the plant life has taken over. He is quickly caught in Poison Ivy's trap. While the vile villainess laughs, Batman tries desperately to reach the vine-withering spray on his Utility Belt.

"Oh, Batman, you look divine!" Poison Ivy cries.

Batman frees himself from the vines and wraps Poison Ivy up in the Batrope!

13

Batman and Robin's night is far from over. The Penguin is trying to take over Gotham City Zoo!

Batman arrives just as the thief escapes, using his umbrella-copter. "This bird has flown the coop!" the Penguin screeches.

"Time to go back in your cage," orders the Caped Crusader. He straps into his Bat-Glider and takes flight.

Batman uses his grappling hook to ensnare the feathered fink and bring him in for a crash landing.

Meanwhile, Mr Freeze has turned the Gotham City Diamond Exchange into a block of ice. The villain freezes Robin in his tracks.

Batman follows Robin's distress call to the scene. He sticks an exploding Batarang into the ice wall, and the blast creates an avalanche that covers Mr Freeze, knocking him out cold. Batman frees Robin using his Laser Cutter.

"That is so *cool*!" smiles Robin, as the ice melts.

When the police arrive to round up Mr Freeze, Commissioner Gordon has news for Batman. "Two-Face just robbed the Second National Bank," the policeman says. "We're on it," Batman replies.

The Dynamic Duo quickly catches up to Two-Face and his gang. "We've got *double trouble*, boys!" the criminal roars.

Thinking fast, Batman presses the Batmobile's turbo boost button and slams the getaway van off the road. Robin takes care of the henchmen as the Caped Crusader confronts Two-Face.
"Tell me where the Joker is!" Batman orders.
The bank robber flips his coin, and he tells Batman where the Clown Prince of Crime is hiding.

The heroes drive to the old Funhouse on Gotham Harbour. The Joker flees. "Stay here, Robin", the Dark Knight commands. "The Joker is a tricky foe!"

Batman leaps out of the Batmobile and runs after the jeering jester. The chase is on!

Batman follows the Joker's cackle into the Hall of Mirrors. Inside, the Caped Crusader is surrounded by several laughing faces. But which one is the real deal? "Looks like *this* Joker is *wild*! *Hahahaha*!" the madman screams.
Batman attacks the one Joker that is different from the others.

The Joker throws an exploding deck of cards at Batman and disappears in a cloud of green smoke. Running out of the back exit, the Joker hops onto his Joker Ski, but it won't start!

Outside the Funhouse, Robin is waiting with the police. He holds up the spark plug he removed from the engine in the Joker Ski.

"Looks like the joke's on you!" Robin laughs.

As the Joker is led back to Arkham Asylum, the Dynamic Duo prepares for the next mission. "To the Batcave!" Batman and Robin shout together.

THE END

Dark Draw

Create your own awesome artwork of Batman by copying this picture one square at a time into the grid below. Now add some colour!

DID YOU KNOW?

Batman's costume, the Batsuit, not only hides his true identity — it also strikes fear into the hearts of his enemies.

Cat Catch!

Batman is racing after Catwoman in the Batmobile. Help him make his way through the mean streets of Gotham City to capture his feline foe!

You can pass through the bat-symbols. Use the route with the MOST symbols.

START

FINISH

ANSWER ON PAGE 69

BATMAN

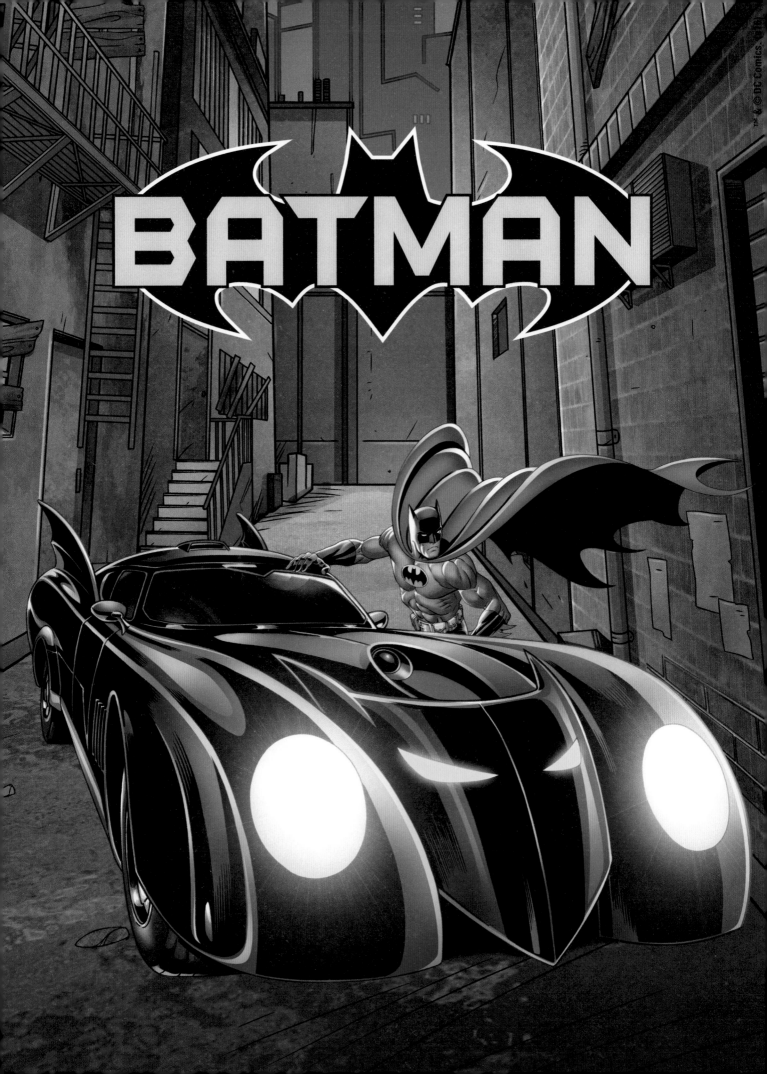

BATMAN VS MAN-BAT

The Caped Crusader is fighting Man-Bat on top of the Gotham City Police Department building! Take a look at the close-up images at the bottom of the page - tick each of the ones you can see in the main picture.

DID YOU KNOW?

Man-Bat was once a scientist named Dr Kirk Langstrom. He tried to cure his deafness with a special serum, but turned himself into a monster that was half-human, half-bat!

ANSWERS ON PAGE 69

A

B

C

D

E

F

G

BEST OF THE BELT!

He is strong and clever, but Batman wouldn't always be able to defeat his enemies without the gadgets on his Utility Belt. Here are a few of the most important ones.

BATARANGS

Shaped like a bat, these sleek weapons are like mega-powerful boomerangs. When Batman throws a Batarang he can cut through obstacles and do some serious damage! The electric Batarang gives a powerful shock. The exploding Batarang blows up when it strikes its target!

REBREATHER

If Batman is trapped underwater, this device allows him to breathe. A small, but life-saving, piece of kit.

GRAPNEL GUN

Designed for scaling tall buildings, it features a super-strong clamp and a cable that can be rewound manually.

MINIATURIZED BAT-TOOLKIT

This hugely useful little device isn't your average toolkit! It features a number of mini-tools that can cut, screw, twist, scrape, pierce and tear!

STUN GUN

This taser is used to temporarily paralyse any enemies. It's a stunning piece of equipment!

MINI-COMPUTER

A highly sophisticated gadget that allows Batman to hack into computers. He can also use it to control power supplies if he needs to disable electric doors and fences.

LASER

This small but effective device fires a laser beam that cuts through almost anything. It's extremely handy when trying to escape from an enclosed space!

ALSO ON THE BELT...

GRENADES: These handy devices produce little fires that can burn through obstacles standing in the Caped Crusader's way.

BATROPE: Can be hurled around the feet of enemies to bring them crashing to the floor!

SMOKE PELLETS: A sudden cloud of smoke can confuse villains and allow a speedy escape!

 # Lock Shock

Commissioner Gordon has been locked in a bank vault. Batman needs your help to break the vault's code before the air inside runs out! One digit from each puzzle forms that all-important code. Get to it!

A BOX CLEVER

Fill in the missing numbers in these boxes. The total number on each line, going across and down, should add up to 15.

5	4	
8		
		4

B ALL SQUARE

This one is a bit trickier. Each row, column and corner box must contain the numbers 1, 2, 3 and 4.

	1	4	
			2
	3		

C TAKE THREE

Which three numbers on this triangle add up to 15? The largest number you use is the final digit in the code.

VAULT CODE

The numbers that will open the vault are:

▼ ▼ ▼

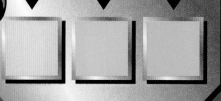

ANSWERS ON PAGE 69

Comic Creator!

Create your very own comic strip by writing in the speech bubbles on the pictures below!

Think Twice!

They may look the same, but there are six differences between these two pictures of Batman fighting Two-Face. Can you spot them all?

ANSWERS ON PAGE 69

The PENGUIN

This criminal mastermind is no birdbrain!

SNEAK BEAKS

As his name suggests, the Penguin loves birds – and trains them to commit crimes!

ESSENTIAL DATA

REAL NAME: Oswald Chesterfield Cobblepot

APPEARANCE: Short and round with a beaky nose

SKILLS: The Penguin is highly intelligent. He runs his criminal empire from his glamorous nightclub, The Iceberg Lounge

WEAPON OF CHOICE: Umbrellas, containing different and dangerous gadgets and weapons

OSWALD'S ORIGINS

As a child, Oswald Cobblepot was bullied a lot at school. When his rich family rejected him, he became the dangerous criminal genius, The Penguin.

BATMAN
FOWL PLAY

Gotham City is suffering from an outbreak of robberies. Citizens everywhere have had valuable possessions stolen from their homes.

Each crime has turned up one odd clue – bird feathers. This one is no different. Batman pockets the feather and heads back to his hide-out.

The Batcave is located directly beneath Wayne Manor. Batman analyses all the feathers he has collected.

"Master Bruce, this may be of interest to you," Alfred says. The butler points to a news report on the Batcomputer.

BYE-BYE BIRDIE

"Gotham City's birds have not returned from their migrations," explains Beverly Birdsong, a worried environmentalist. "This is not natural. Something is wrong."

"Hmm, I bet these events are connected somehow," Bruce says.

Suddenly, an alarm sounds in Wayne Manor. There must be an intruder! Bruce and Alfred race to the study to see a vulture fly out of a broken window. Its talons are carrying an upside-down umbrella containing Bruce Wayne's expensive gold watch, mobile phone and laptop.

"Must I remind you not to leave your toys lying around?" Alfred says.

"Don't worry, old friend," Bruce replies. "All of those items have tracking devices. The latest in Wayne Enterprises technology."

Alfred nods. "And they'll lead us straight to the mystery mastermind behind this crooked caper." With no time to lose, the two friends head back to the Batcave.

Bruce puts on his Batsuit, packs his Utility Belt, and takes off in the Batplane. He follows the tracking signals to the Iceberg Lounge, a nightclub owned by the gangster, Oswald Cobblepot.

Several birds fly in through a skylight, all carrying umbrellas. The Caped Crusader lands on the roof. Then he follows the birds inside.

Batman finds his way to Oswald Cobblepot's private office. The little looter hops up to greet the Caped Crusader. "I'll have you know this is an exclusive club," he cackles. "Not all flying creatures are welcome."

"Mr Cobblepot, I presume?" asks Batman. "So you're the one behind all this fowl play."

"Yes," squawks Oswald. "But you can call me the PENGUIN!"

"What's your game, Penguin?" the hero asks.

The villain narrows his beady eyes and smiles. "Since you won't be getting out alive, I'll tell you. My fine-feathered friends are helping me become the richest man in Gotham. Soon I'll move into Wayne Manor and kick Bruce Wayne to the curb!"

"The only big house you'll be going to... is Blackgate Penitentiary!" Batman replies.

The Penguin blows on a whistle, commanding the birds' attention. In an instant, the flying furies descend on Batman. They peck and scratch and claw at the Caped Crusader.

"I've spent all winter hypnotizing these wonderful creatures to do my bidding," the greedy gangster explains. "Now I'll have them rid me of my rodent infestation, once and for all!"

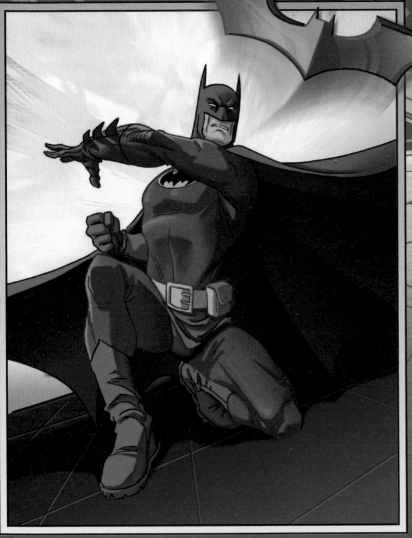

Batman needs to stop the birds without hurting them. Thinking quickly, he hurls a Batarang at the sprinkler system, releasing a torrent of water. The birds snap out of their trance and fly out of the skylight.

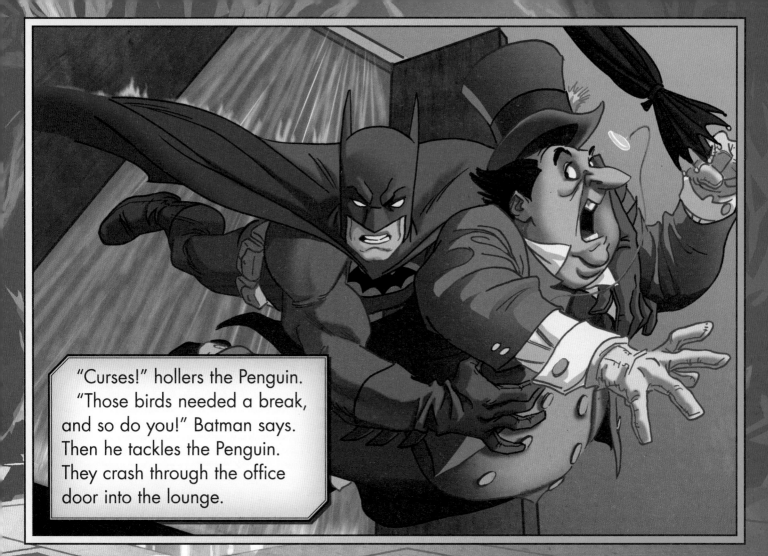

"Curses!" hollers the Penguin. "Those birds needed a break, and so do you!" Batman says. Then he tackles the Penguin. They crash through the office door into the lounge.

As they hit the ground, the villain whips out his trick umbrella. He points the end at Batman and sprays him with gas. The hero is momentarily disoriented.

Then the Penguin's wicked weapon transforms into an umbrella-jet pack! It lifts the foe up over the ballroom towards another skylight.

"Penguins do not fly unless it is with style!" the villain taunts, as he makes his escape.

"It's time to put this turkey on ice," Batman says with a growl. He reaches into his Utility Belt and pulls out another gadget – a freeze bomb. The Caped Crusader throws the device at the fancy fountain down below.

Upon impact, the freeze bomb explodes. The giant seal sculpture erupts and a wave of water washes over the Penguin. The chemicals within the bomb freeze the water, instantly trapping the villain.

Minutes later, the police arrive. Batman tells Commissioner Gordon that the Penguin had trained the birds to steal by flying in and out of homes. That was the reason they never found a culprit.

"Your help is much appreciated, Batman," says Commissioner Gordon. "Thank you."

"It was nothing," Batman replies. "I love a good mystery!"

Two officers climb up to chisel the cold criminal out of his frozen prison. Then they will transfer the Penguin to a more permanent home at Blackgate Penitentiary. After that, all the stolen valuables will be returned to their rightful owners.

The next day, Bruce and Alfred go bird-watching with Beverly Birdsong. "I'm so glad these beautiful birds are flying free!" she says, as a vulture soars high above the trees.

Alfred agrees, but Bruce is not so sure. "Oh, I can think of one bird that belongs in a cage," he says with a smile. "The Penguin!"

THE END

Riddle Me This ? ? ?

The cunning Riddler has come up with some bamboozling brain-teasers. Can you solve them before he wreaks havoc on Gotham City?

What gets wetter the more it dries?....
Clue: You'll find it in the bathroom....

What sort of room can no one enter?....
Clue: It looks good enough to eat....

The more you take away, the larger it grows. What is it?....
Clue: You'll have to dig yourself out of this one....

RIDDLE 1

"I've teamed up with one of Batman's enemies to bring mayhem to the streets of Gotham City. But who is it? Put the letters below in the right order to find out..."

C O W R A C E R S

[ ][ ][ ][ ][ ][ ][ ][ ][ ]

RIDDLE 2

"We've hidden a ticking time-bomb in a building. Start at the G and move up, down, left or right to spell out the location in the grid. Every letter is used once - and once only!"

START

G	O	T
I	C	H
T	M	A
Y	H	A
T	N	L
O	W	L

FINISH

RIDDLE 3

"Batman can easily deactivate the bomb. He just needs to find the right room first! If you put the letters below in the right gaps you'll find out the location."

C I T N E

| K | | | | H | | |

ANSWERS ON PAGE 69

39

Mission: Man-bat

YOUR MISSION

Gotham City is in trouble. Man-Bat is on a night-time rampage and he's moving fast. Help Batman locate his foe quickly by completing these three mazes.

TRICKY TRAIL

Killer Croc has teamed up with Man-Bat. You can help Batman and Robin find and defeat him by solving this maze. Move from character to character in this order: Batman, Killer Croc, Robin, Man-Bat and back to Batman to start the sequence again. You can move up, down, left or right but never diagonally. Start in the top left corner and find the shortest trail to Batman in the bottom right corner.

START

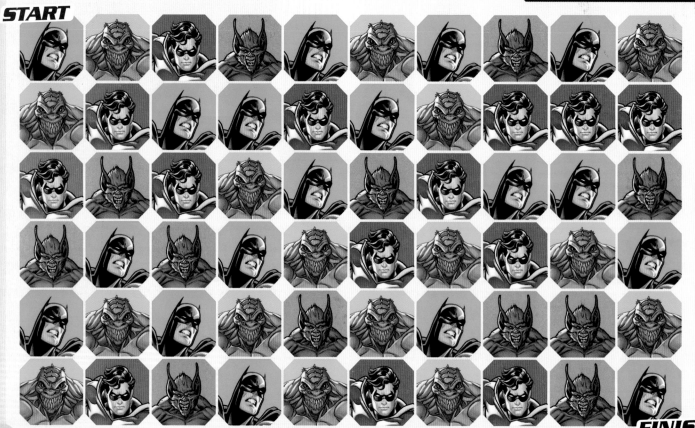

FINISH

TANGLED UP

There are four possible routes to the next location on the journey to finding Man-Bat. Can you find the correct one?

A

B

C

D

START

FINAL COUNTDOWN

You're almost there. Travel through the tunnels under Gotham City and you will have tracked down Man-Bat. Batman has conquered his enemy again!

▶ FINISH

41

ROGUES GALLERY

They're dangerous, sinister and cause the Dark Knight plenty of problems. Here are four of Gotham City's nastiest pieces of work...

DID YOU KNOW?

Two-Face doesn't believe in right and wrong, He believes in chance. That's why he always flips a special coin when he has to make a decision. Heads or tails?

SCARECROW

ESSENTIAL DATA

REAL NAME: Dr Jonathan Crane

APPEARANCE: The scariest scarecrow... ever!

SKILLS: As a former professor of human behaviour, the Scarecrow uses mind games to terrify his enemies. He can also mutate into a hideous monster called the Scarebeast. He enjoys chaos and is completely immune to fear

WEAPON OF CHOICE: Fear gas that makes victims see their worst nightmares as if they were real

Two-Face

ESSENTIAL DATA

REAL NAME: Harvey Dent

APPEARANCE: A smart-suited, two-faced horror

SKILLS: Once a District Attorney of Gotham City, Dent went mad after a gangster threw acid in his face. He became a criminal genius. Two-Face is also skilled at hand-to-hand combat

WEAPON OF CHOICE: Two semi-automatic pistols

The Riddler

ESSENTIAL DATA

REAL NAME: Edward Nigma

APPEARANCE: Green, dapper... and covered in question marks

SKILLS: Vast knowledge and great intelligence. An expert puzzle-creator and mind-game player

WEAPON OF CHOICE: His incredible brain, though he does sometimes use exploding jigsaw pieces and his question mark-shaped cane!

KILLER CROC

ESSENTIAL DATA

REAL NAME: Waylon Jones

APPEARANCE: Mean, green monster!

SKILLS: The disease that turned Jones into a reptile mutant has given Killer Croc super-human strength, speed, agility and reflexes. He also has a reptile's ability for quick healing

WEAPON OF CHOICE: His own strength

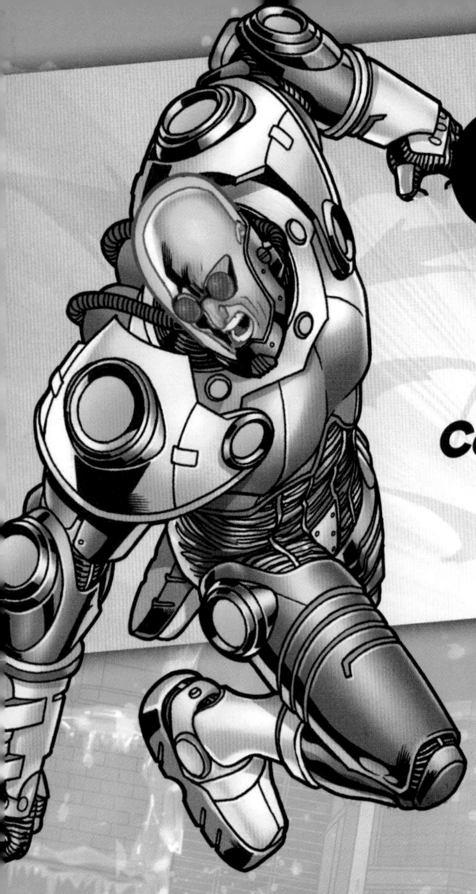

Cold Storage

Mr Freeze has frozen Robin, as well as Two-Face, the Penguin and the Scarecrow. Can you identify who is inside each block of ice and write their names underneath?

DID YOU KNOW?

Also known as Dr Victor Fries, Mr Freeze is famous for covering anyone who gets in his way with ice.

A

B

C

D

ANSWERS ON PAGE 69

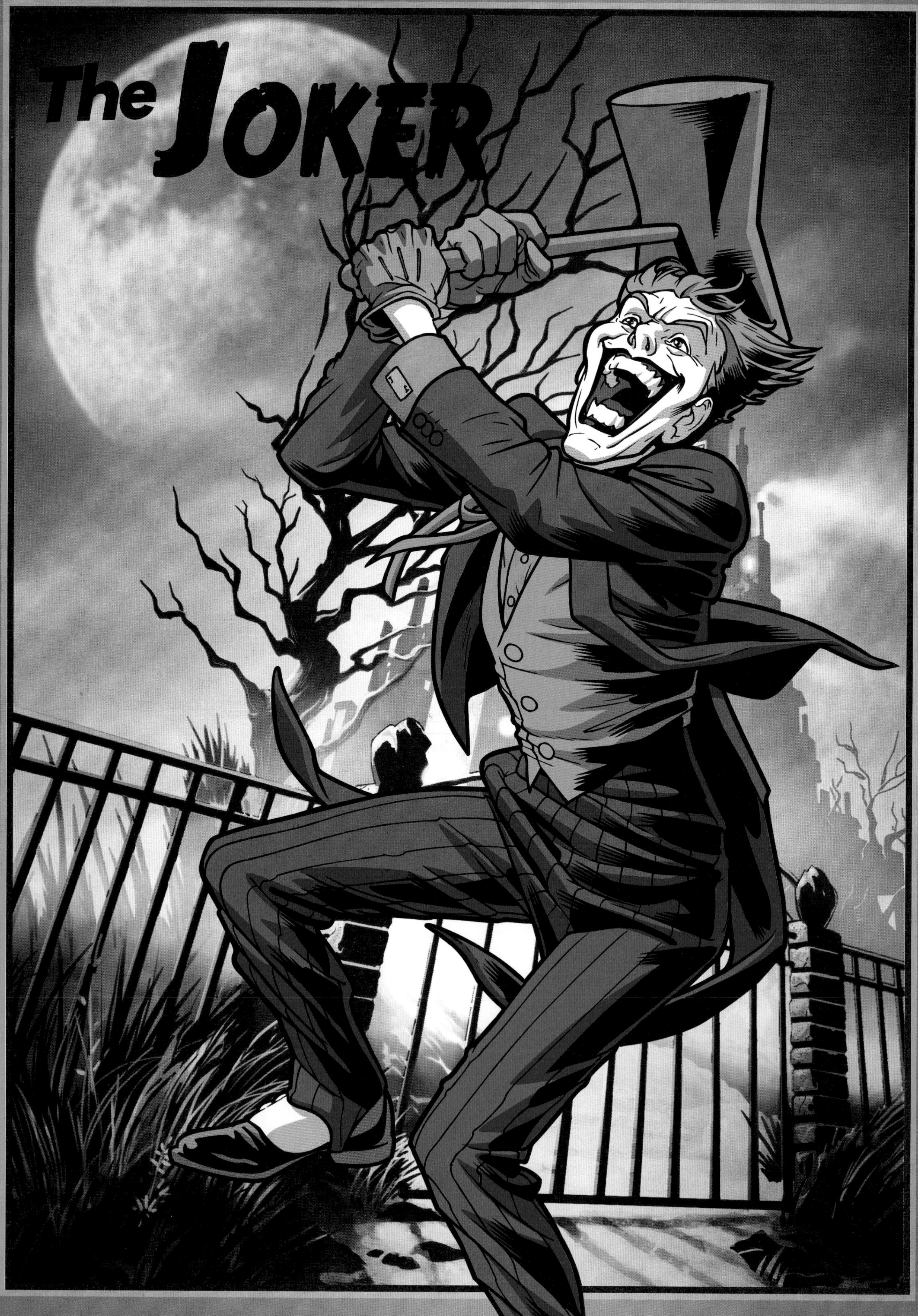
The JOKER

Double Trouble!

Using the small picture to help you, colour in Two-Face, Gotham City's own double dose of danger.

DID YOU KNOW?

Two-Face isn't just skilled at planning crazy crimes – he's also an expert at kung fu.

Utility Belt Dash!

The contents of Batman's Utility Belt have been dropped around Gotham City. Pick up as many items as you can while avoiding the enemies.

YOU WILL NEED

- Two to four players
- Counters - cut out the ones below or use buttons or bottle caps
- Pens
- Paper
- A dice

INSTRUCTIONS

Each player picks a character counter and places it on START. Take turns throwing the dice and moving your counter up the board to the Batcave.

If you land on one of the eight Utility Belt items, collect it by writing its name on your piece of paper. All items can be collected by more than one player. No player can hold a duplicate of any item.

If you land on a Batmobile space, collect one item you don't already own.

If you land on a Villain square, follow the instructions.

The game ends when all players are at the Batcave. You do not need an exact number to finish. The winner is the player who has collected the most items. If it's a tie, start the game again – the winner is the first player to collect a Utility Belt item they don't already have!

46	47 Rebreather
45 The Penguin	44
36	37 Poison Ivy
35 Mini-Computer	34
24 Bat-Toolkit	25
23	22 The Penguin
12	13
11	10 Poison Ivy
START	1 Killer Croc

48

49 The Joker

50

FINISH

43

42

41 Catwoman

38

39 Bat Drone

40

33

32

31

30 Killer Croc

26 Mr Freeze

27

28 Batarang

29

21

20

19 Grapnel Gun

18

14 Catwoman

15

16

17 The Joker

9

8 Laser

7

6 Mr Freeze

2

3

4 Stun Gun

5

VILLAIN SQUARES

CATWOMAN
trips you over with her whip. Swap places with the player in front of you.

KILLER CROC
gives you a gentle nudge – and sends you forward 4 spaces!

POISON IVY
gives you a nasty plant toxin that confuses you. Double your next throw.

MR FREEZE
ices your hands. You're unable to collect the next Belt item you land on.

THE PENGUIN
injures you with his poison-tip umbrella. Go forward 3 spaces for treatment.

THE JOKER
is up to his tricks. Lose one of your Utility Belt items (if you've collected any).

49

Crack The Code

Batman is being held hostage by the Penguin, but he's sent Robin a message that reveals his location. Can you help the Boy Wonder solve the code?

1 SECRET SYMBOLS

Take a look at Robin's symbol key and match the symbols Batman sent with the correct letters to decode the first word.

A D E N H R T W

2 NUMBER CODE

Swap numbers for letters for the second word.

1	2	3
I	E	G
4	5	6
R	B	C

1	6	2	5	2	4	3

3 CROSS-OUT CODE

Cross out all the red and blue boxes. Rearrange the letters left behind to reveal the final word of the location.

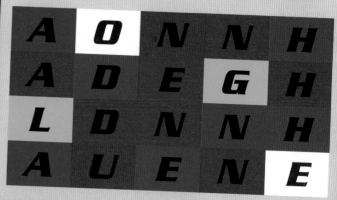

BATMAN IS BEING HELD AT:

ANSWERS ON PAGE 69

CATWOMAN

She's almost the purr-fect criminal...

ESSENTIAL DATA

REAL NAME: Selina Kyle

APPEARANCE: No surprises with the catsuit – plus a mask shaped like cat ears!

SKILLS: Highly athletic and super-fit, this foe is one skilled and deadly burglar

WEAPON OF CHOICE: A cat o' nine tails whip – and better watch out for those sharp claws!

TROUBLED PAST

Selina had a difficult childhood and turned to burglary to survive.

BAT AND CAT

Selina began wearing a catsuit as a disguise after seeing Batman early on in her criminal career. She decided that if he can dress like a bat, she can dress like a cat!

FRIEND OR FOE

Catwoman and the Caped Crusader have also worked together as allies!

51

FELINE FELONIES

Deep in the night, two dark shadows move across the Gotham City rooftops. One of them is Batman. He follows the trail of an elusive cat burglar to Wayne Towers.

Batman lands on the balcony of the penthouse. Inside is the Golden Cat, a statue so rare and valuable few have ever seen it. Only one thief in Gotham City would dare to attempt such a cat-themed robbery.

"It ends here, Catwoman!" growls the Caped Crusader.

The thief steps into the moonlight. But it's not Catwoman – it's the Cheetah! Batman is stunned.

"They say you're the World's Greatest Detective, but I'm not impressed," hisses the feline felon. "Out of my way. I've got a city to rob!"

The Cheetah tries to slash Batman with her sharp claws, but he uses his cape to protect himself.

With catlike speed, the Cheetah leaps off the balcony into the darkness. Batman quickly throws a Bat-Tracker onto the escaping villainess.

The Caped Crusader contacts Wonder Woman from his Batmobile. "Your arch-enemy almost made me her new scratching post," Batman says. "The Cheetah is in Gotham City?" Wonder Woman exclaims.

Minutes later, Wonder Woman lands her Invisible Jet on the roof of the Gotham City Museum, where Batman is waiting for her.

"My Bat-Tracker led me here," says Batman. "The Cat's Eye Opal is on display and worth millions." "Let's pounce!" Wonder Woman replies.

The Cheetah breaks into the dark museum only to discover that Gotham City's original cat burglar, Catwoman, is already on the scene... and she has her paws on the famous gem!

"And who might you be?" Catwoman asks.

"I'm the Cheetah," says the villainess. "And you're stealing my Cat's Eye!"

Catwoman raises her claws and hisses. "Come any closer, and this won't be the only cat's eye you lose!"

"Mee-ouch!" the Cheetah snaps back.

The night-watchmen hear the catfight and sound the alarm.

"Time to crash this party!" Batman says.

"Look what the Cheetah dragged in!" Catwoman snarls.
The Caped Crusader and the Amazon Princess face off against their feline foes. The cat burglars have to work together to get out of this tight spot.

The Cheetah and Catwoman grab the guards and take them hostage.
"Not another step," the Cheetah yells.
"Or else!" Catwoman finishes.
The heroes must allow the criminals to go, in order to save the hostages.

Back on the roof, Batman is angry at this turn of events.
"We can still find them with your Bat-Tracker," Wonder
Woman says.
"That's true," says Batman. "I have a plan." He looks at the
Invisible Jet and smiles. "They won't know what hit them!"

Across town, Catwoman and the Cheetah
are now working together to steal the white
tiger from the Gotham City Zoo.
"Such a beautiful and powerful creature
doesn't belong in a cage," Catwoman purrs.
"Let's train her to do our bidding!" the
Cheetah exclaims.

As Catwoman picks the lock, she
is startled by a flying Batarang.
The felines scan the darkness but
the heroes are nowhere to be seen.
"Show yourself, Batman!" says
Catwoman. "I know you found us
with some sort of Bat-gadget."
"I bet they're hiding in that
blasted Invisible Jet," the Cheetah
warns her new ally.

"Not anymore," says a voice. Wonder Woman appears behind the Cheetah and knocks her to the ground.

Catwoman cracks her whip at Wonder Woman's feet. The hero twirls her Golden Lasso. "Two can play at this game!"

The battle is fierce, but Catwoman is no match for the Amazon Princess. She uses the unbreakable Lasso to tie up the burglar.

Meanwhile, the Cheetah runs into the lion's den. The Caped Crusader emerges from the shadows and swings high overhead. He won't let her get away again.

Batman lands in front of the scoundrel, blocking her escape. The great cats come to her aid and surround Batman.

"Ready for round two?" the Cheetah asks, and prepares to strike.

This time, Batman is faster than the Cheetah. He throws a smoke bomb, releasing a cloud of sleeping gas. When the air clears, all the felines are taking a catnap.

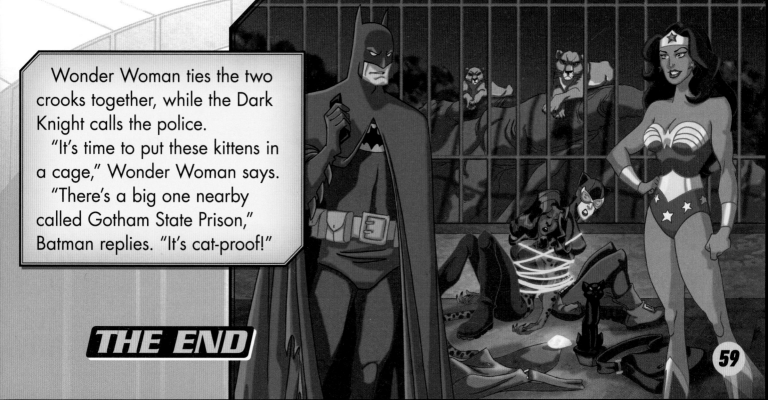

Wonder Woman ties the two crooks together, while the Dark Knight calls the police.

"It's time to put these kittens in a cage," Wonder Woman says.

"There's a big one nearby called Gotham State Prison," Batman replies. "It's cat-proof!"

THE END

Hidden Enemies

Batman's famous foes are hiding in this grid. Names run forwards, backwards, up, down, diagonally and back-to-front! Can you find them all?

N	I	B	O	R	Y	T	B	A	P	N	M	M	J	N
S	M	L	L	U	V	E	C	A	T	W	O	M	A	N
K	A	Y	C	R	I	R	R	L	C	I	K	G	S	E
E	G	E	J	G	N	M	O	E	S	C	W	Z	C	B
G	N	N	Z	E	O	A	R	H	N	O	F	O	L	E
O	M	A	C	E	S	T	M	F	R	F	R	K	A	N
T	O	L	B	A	I	S	H	C	R	C	O	V	Y	Y
H	R	F	S	U	O	L	E	A	R	E	P	M	F	A
A	A	R	A	M	P	R	R	E	L	B	E	W	A	W
M	U	E	R	J	A	I	L	B	A	P	N	Z	C	E
C	O	D	T	C	D	L	U	T	I	E	G	A	E	C
I	F	G	S	D	I	H	M	I	D	N	U	O	A	U
T	N	H	L	K	P	A	I	U	A	G	I	C	Z	R
Y	P	E	K	P	N	D	C	M	L	M	N	H	C	B
P	R	R	E	K	O	J	K	S	W	O	O	J	S	T

  BANE

 CATWOMAN

 CLAYFACE

JOKER

 KILLER CROC

 MR FREEZE

 PENGUIN

 POISON IVY

 RIDDLER

 SCARECROW

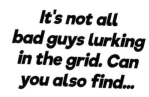

It's not all bad guys lurking in the grid. Can you also find...

ALFRED

BATMAN

BRUCE WAYNE

GOTHAM CITY

ROBIN

ANSWERS ON PAGE 69

Ally Match

Which of Batman's allies are you most like? This quiz will help you find out.

START

Which of these do you rely on most?

STRENGTH → Are you ace at video games?

BRAINS → Are you good with food?

I DON'T PLAY THAT OFTEN → If a friend was in trouble, what would you do?

I'M AN EXPERT ... AT EATING! → If a friend was in trouble, what would you do?

I'M A LEGEND!

I'D LOVE TO BE A TOP CHEF

RUSH IN TO HELP

FORM A PLAN OF ACTION

Can you keep secrets?

I TELL IT AS IT IS → Are you good at sports?

Are you good at first aid?

I TAKE CONTROL WHEN NEEDED

Do you prefer to lead or follow?

SURE, I LEAD A DOUBLE LIFE!

I'M AN ALL-ROUND ATHLETE

I PREFER TO WATCH

I OFTEN NEED TO RECEIVE IT!

YES, I COULD BE A DOCTOR

I'M HAPPY TAKING ORDERS

ROBIN

You're always there to help out, but fearless enough to take on any trouble by yourself.

COMMISSIONER GORDON

A safe pair of hands, always willing to go the extra mile, you're a reliable, brave pal.

ALFRED

You're clever and cautious. Your friends know they can always come to you for sensible advice.

61

VITAL VEHICLES

Batman has some awesome vehicles to help him speed around Gotham City and get to the crooks quickly. Here are four of his finest modes of transport.

BATMOBILE

The Batmobile can fire missiles and is heavily protected from attack.

This cool car has a bunch of incredible gadgets on board, as well as a portable crime laboratory!

Batman has used several versions of the Batmobile to fight crime.

The Dark Knight often uses the Batmobile. It can travel in excess of 200mph – and can reach 350mph with its afterburner thrust. You can see why he likes it so much!

BATCYCLE

Robin often uses the Batcycle on missions.

It has a powerful V4 engine, computer controls, chunky tyres and an autopilot function. Oh, and it looks amazing, too!

This is a street bike that has had a major make-over!

BATBOAT

The Batboat has homing torpedoes and a harpoon. They prove useful if the Caped Crusader needs to defend himself from enemy action!

It has a top speed of 120mph and can even go underwater. its on-board oxygen tanks hold six hours of air.

BATPLANE

The Batplane adjusts to different situations. At 45,000 to 55,000 feet, its fins increase in length to keep it stable as it reaches supersonic speeds.

At its top height of 60,000 feet, 'smart paint' makes the Batplane go stealth. That means it's virtually impossible to see!

File Failure

YOUR MISSION

One of Gotham City's case files has been hacked by cyber-criminals. The report is about a battle between the Dark Knight and Killer Croc, but it is now missing valuable info. Use the words in the list to fill in the gaps and complete the report. Each word is used only once.

y:76.3341IY
x:987.411Y

LOCK TARGET
TARGET

KILLER CROC REPORT

What seemed like a _ _ _ _ _ day in Gotham City was ruined when

Batman received a _ _ _ _ _ _ _ _ call from Robin. The loyal friend

and _ _ _ _ _ _ _ _ _ of the _ _ _ _ _ Crusader was at the Police

_ _ _ _ _ _ _ _ _ _ when suddenly Killer Croc went on the rampage.

Offices in the building were being wrecked as the dangerous foe

_ _ _ _ _ _ _ _ around looking for Commissioner _ _ _ _ _ _ _ , shouting something about "Revenge"! Batman summoned the Batmobile and quickly sped to _ _ _ _ _ _ _ _ Gotham City. He climbed up the police HQ building using his Grapnel Gun. After _ _ _ _ _ _ _ _ the room Killer Croc was lurking in, Batman alerted Robin and arranged a double-attack.

First of all, Batman _ _ _ _ _ _ _ the glass in the window using a Batarang. Once Batman was _ _ _ _ _ _ the office, Robin arrived and the pair of them unleashed a number of _ _ _ _ _ _ _ on Killer Croc.

The Grapnel Gun tied the villain's legs together. Then Batman hurled an electric _ _ _ _ _ _ _ _ to electrify Killer Croc. This gave Batman and Robin a chance to summon help from the police officers, who placed steel _ _ _ _ _ _ on the enemy's wrists and _ _ _ _ _ _ and carted him away.

WORD LIST

ankles	charged	distress	inside	smashed
Batarang	clamps	downtown	quiet	spotting
Caped	Department	Gordon	sidekick	weapons

Copy Car!

Draw the Batmobile, the coolest car in Gotham City!
Copy the picture into the empty grid one square at a time.
Make your drawing really awesome by colouring it in.

DID YOU KNOW?

Some of the items that have been in the Batmobile over the years include inflatable rubber rafts, a Batphone that connects to police headquarters and a first-aid kit!

ANSWERS ON PAGE 69

ROAD RIDDLE

Help Batman get across the city. Move along one square that can be divided by 5 or 7 in each column.

2	15	18	22	23	28
7	13	12	14	25	31
9	6	10	11	17	27

Testing Time

How well do you know Batman, his gadgets and his enemies? All of the answers are somewhere inside this annual!

1 WHAT MADE YOUNG BRUCE WAYNE WANT TO FIGHT CRIME?

A Witnessing his parents' murder

B Being attacked at school

C Failing football trials

2 WHAT HAPPENS TO THE BATPLANE WHEN IT REACHES 60,000 FEET?

A It explodes

B It can travel at the speed of light

C It enters stealth mode

3 WHERE DOES BATMAN STORE GADGETS AND EQUIPMENT?

A Utility Belt

B Utility Briefcase

C Utility Backpack

4 WHAT IS THE SCARECROW'S REAL NAME?

A Dr Harvey Swann

B Dr I M Strawman

C Dr Jonathan Crane

5 WHAT WAS HARVEY DENT'S JOB BEFORE HE BECAME TWO-FACE?

A District Attorney of Gotham City

B A round-the-world sailor

C A Gotham City police officer

6 WHAT SYMBOL IS THE RIDDLER FAMOUS FOR?

A Question mark

B Comma

C Exclamation mark

7 WHAT WEAPONS DOES THE BATBOAT CARRY?

A Cruise missiles

B Homing torpedoes and a harpoon

C Poison pilchards

8 WHAT IS THE JOKER'S WEAPON OF CHOICE?

A Joker Poker

B Joker Venom

C Joker Tank

9 WHAT IS THE NAME OF THE PENGUIN'S NIGHTCLUB?

A The Frozen Fortress

B The Iceberg Lounge

C The Cool Club

10 WHAT CRIME IS CATWOMAN BEST KNOWN FOR?

A Burglary

B Noise pollution

C Hacking computers

ANSWERS ON PAGE 69

Super-Villain!

Once you've worked out who this monster is made from, come up with a name for him!

This beastie mash-up is made from five of the Dark Knight's fiercest foes. Identify which parts come from the Joker, Killer Croc, Man-Bat, the Penguin and the Riddler.

HAT:

HEAD:

CHEST:

ARMS:

LEGS:

SUPER-VILLAIN NAME:

IN THE SHADOWS

This Gotham City nasty isn't part of the monster villain. But can you match the Scarecrow to his shadow?

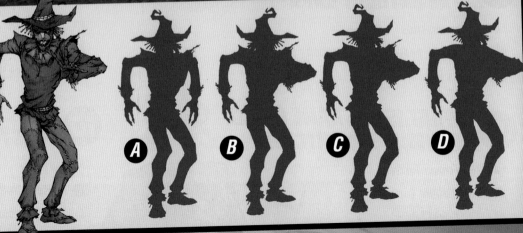

A   B   C   D

ANSWERS ON PAGE 69

Answers

Page 8
PIECE OF THE ACTION!
A1, B10, C5, D7

Page 20
CAT CATCH!

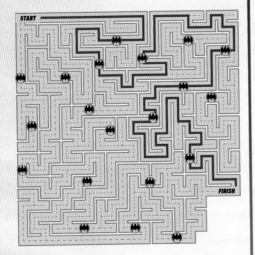

Page 23
BATMAN VS MAN-BAT
B, C, F, G

Page 26
LOCK SHOCK

A.
5	4	6
8	2	5
2	9	4

B.
2	1	4	3
3	4	2	1
1	2	3	4
4	3	1	2

C. 6 + 4 + 5 = 15
Vault code: 9 1 6

Page 28
THINK TWICE!

Page 39
RIDDLE ME THIS
1. Scarecrow
2. Gotham City Town Hall
3. Kitchen
Favourite Riddles:
Mushroom, Hole
and Towel

Pages 40-41
MISSION: MAN-BAT
TRICKY TRAIL:

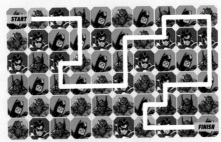

TANGLED UP: Route C
FINAL COUNTDOWN:

Page 44
COLD STORAGE
A. The Penguin
B. Two-Face
C. Scarecrow
D. Robin

Page 50
CRACK THE CODE
The Iceberg Lounge

Page 60
HIDDEN ENEMIES

N	I	B	O	R	Y	T	B	A	P	N	M	M	J	N
S	M	L	L	U	V	E	C	A	T	W	O	M	A	N
K	A	Y	C	R	I	R	R	L	C	I	K	G	S	E
E	G	E	J	G	N	M	O	E	S	C	W	Z	C	B
G	N	N	Z	E	O	A	R	H	N	O	F	O	L	E
O	M	A	C	E	S	T	M	F	R	F	R	K	A	N
T	O	L	B	A	I	S	H	C	R	C	O	V	V	Y
H	R	F	S	U	O	L	E	A	R	E	P	M	F	A
A	A	R	A	M	P	R	R	E	L	B	E	W	A	W
M	U	E	R	J	A	I	L	B	A	P	N	Z	C	E
C	O	O	D	T	C	D	L	U	T	I	E	G	A	E
I	F	G	S	D	I	H	M	I	D	N	U	O	A	U
T	N	H	L	K	P	A	I	U	A	G	I	C	Z	R
Y	P	E	K	P	N	D	C	M	L	M	N	H	C	B
P	R	R	E	K	O	J	K	S	W	O	O	J	S	T

Pages 64-65
FILE FAILURE
The missing words
in order are: quiet,
distress, sidekick, Caped,
Department, charged,
Gordon, downtown,
spotting, smashed,
inside, weapons,
Batarang, clamps, ankles

Page 66
ROAD RIDDLE
The correct route is:
7, 15, 10, 14, 25, 28

Page 67
TESTING TIME
1A, 2C, 3A, 4C, 5A,
6A, 7B, 8B, 9B, 10A

Page 68
SUPER-VILLAIN
Hat: The Riddler
Head: The Joker
Chest: Killer Croc
Arms: The Penguin
Legs: Man-Bat

IN THE SHADOWS
C